First English language edition published in 1988 by Barron's Educational Series

The Giraffe

Illustrations : Anne Leduc
Text : Nadine Saunier

 CHILDRENS PRESS CHOICE

A Barron's title selected for educational distribution

ISBN 0-516-08527-1

From a height of ⬚ yards,
the long-necked giraffe chews her cud.
Her touching eyes, rimmed with thick lashes,
are always on the alert.
From far away,
the designs of her ⬚ ,

spotted with ⬚ and brown,
blend with the surrounding vegetation.

Some of the words in this book are replaced by pictures.
These pictures reappear and are identified at the end of the book.

The giraffe strolls from one to the other.
Her long, raspy tongue, which doesn't
even feel the prickles of the thorns,
wraps around the

and the stems
of the acacia tree.
To keep her coat clean and shiny,
she rubs against the trunks.

Not far from a termite's nest

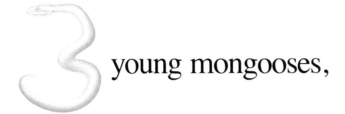 young mongooses,

sit up attentively, to watch a
male and female giraffe   .

What a dance they do! They slowly rub again
each other while their long necks intertwine.
The giraffes are silent.

More than a year later,

a  , about six feet tall, is born.

He falls to the ground with all his weight,
because his mother gives birth standing up.
For ten months, he drinks

the rich ⎍ of his mother.
She often leaves him in the nursery,
watched by other adult females.

The  doesn't know how to swim.
To drink, she spreads her front legs far apart,
bends her knees slightly,
and lowers her head to the water.
It's often near water
that s lie in wait.

To defend herself
or protect her   ,
the giraffe kicks out powerfully
with her hooves.
Giraffes are feared
and are not attacked very often.

s live in a herd.

When they travel, they walk along at the same pace,

each lifting both legs on one side,

then both legs on the other side.

What a light and elegant picture they make,

despite a  of nearly a ton!

Sometimes the males fight among themselves
over who will lead the herd.

They take places ⌐ next to the other
and keep their balance
by spreading their back legs apart.
Then they begin to push.

The blows
      of their   are very loud
but rarely cause injury.

The giraffe never .
It sleeps little; instead it dozes,
its neck folded against its back.
Of all the animals,

the smallest is the ,

the largest is the ,

and the tallest is the .

five

coat

orange

in love

baby giraffe

milk

flea

weight

elephant

tree

leaves

three

lion

giraffe

one

baby giraffe

horns

lies down

giraffe

giraffe

Library of Congress Catalog Card No. 87-072555
International Standard Book No. 0-8120-5930-1   PRINTED IN ITALY

ANIMAL- GIRAFFE

Saunier, Nadine
The Giraffe